MW00884801

THE ADVENTURES OF

DASH JACKSON

I Like To Imagine

BY NICHOLE JACKSON

ILLUSTRATED BY CAMERON WILSON

First Edition November 2020

Book Written By Nichole Jackson
Illustration By Cameron Wilson

The author gratefully acknowledges the editorial contributions of Lakeya Tucker

ISBN 978-0-578-75302-7 (hardcover)

Published By DNA Publishing Inc
www.adventuresofdashjackson.com

TO ASH AND DASH!
YOU ARE MY MOTIVATION AND INSPIRATION!

My name is Dash! I love spending time with my family. Every day is an adventure because we always do fun things together.

I love learning how to do new and exciting things. This morning my mom taught me how to paint. I imagined I was a famous artist with nice pictures in a fancy museum. People even stood in long lines to see my artwork.

After I finished painting, my mom took me to the park. I was excited because there was a big playground, a creek, a nature trail and a huge lake. First, my mom taught me how to fish. We walked over to the lake. We brought all the things we needed like a fishing pole, worms and a net. I have my own special tackle box where I keep all my hooks, bait and other important things I need.

My mom always says, "Being a good fisherman means you have to learn to be patient."

While waiting patiently, I imagined I was a fisherman on a boat in the middle of the ocean. The waves were super high and the fish were gigantic.

I really liked looking at all the different fish swimming in the lake. I imagined I was a marine biologist swimming in the ocean. I had a special swimsuit and other equipment to help me study the fish.

After we finished fishing, we rode our bikes on the nature trail. I am still learning how to ride my bike. I practiced keeping my balance as I rode on the trail. My mom always reminds me to keep peddling, keep my arms straight and to pay attention. "You will get better and better every time you practice Dash. Just keep going and never give up," she yelled.

I imagined I was a professional stunt man riding in a bike show. I imagined I did all kinds of tricks. I did flips and rode on one wheel.

After we finished riding our bikes, we went to the playground. There was a tall slide, swings, monkey bars and a drawbridge. I love to run across the bridge. I imagined I was a knight trying to protect a queen and the kingdom.

After playing on the drawbridge, I played on the monkey bars. I imagined I was a ninja wearing a special fighting suit climbing up the side of buildings all around the city chasing after the bad warriors.

As we walked in the park, we saw a small creek with rocks and small fish. My mom and I decided to go rock jumping. "We have to be very careful and make sure we take our time," my mom warned. We skipped from one rock to the next. I imagined I was inside a volcano trying to jump from side to side skipping over hot lava.

My favorite part of the day was riding the carousal. I rode on the big black horse. I imagined I was cowboy with a big cowboy hat and huge cowboy boots. I imagined I chased after bank robbers.

I imagined I caught the bank robbers and collected my reward, a big ice cream cone from the food cart.

After I ate the ice cream it was time to go home.

On our way to the car, I saw a huge hole in the ground. My mom warned me to move back. "That is a storm drain and it is not safe to go inside the hole Dash," she explained.

I wanted a closer look. I thought if I was very careful, I could get close enough to look all the way down. I did not listen to my mom and instead, I kept walking closer to the hole.

It was very dark inside the hole just like outer space. I imagined I was an astronaut. I imagined I had on a cool space suite with special buttons and gadgets. As I imagined I was flying in outer space, I started spinning and turning. I was not paying attention and I was not being very careful.

As I turned and spun around, I slipped and went falling. I almost fell down into the hole but my mom caught me just in time. I was very scared but my mom held me very tightly and pulled me to safety.

My mom was very unhappy because I did not listen. "It is good to use your imagination and play. Your imagination helps you to see all the possibilities there are. It helps you to see all the things you can do but you must always be safe and follow my rules," she scolded.

When we reached the car, I apologized. I thanked my mom for taking me to the park. I had fun playing on the playground using my imagination but most of all, I was glad my mom helped keep me safe. I really like to imagine all the time. My mom says, "It helps to build your confidence and helps you learn how to do new things."